C000226123

WELSH HISTORY STORIES

JOHN DAVIES AND THE PLAGUE

JOHN EVANS

Illustrated by Francis Phillipps

DREF WEN

It is May 1652. My name is John Davids. In July, I will be ten years old. Haverfordwest is an unhappy place to live in. Since last October, we have suffered a great plague.

Many people have died. Many more are very ill
with this terrible disease. Sometimes they get better,
but usually they die.

My father, Thomas Davids, is the mayor of this town.
Last month he left the town to travel to London.
Some people have said unkind things about him.
They say he has run away from the town, so that
he will not catch the plague.

Mother says they are wrong. He has gone to ask the Lord General Cromwell for help for our people who are suffering so much.

5

Nobody knows what has caused the plague. Every
Sunday we go to church. Our rector, Stephen Love,
says, "The Lord is punishing you all for your
wickedness. You have all been sinful. You have
been telling lies.

You have been swearing and drinking. You have been working on Sundays. Even your children have been spiteful and nasty! You must walk in the ways of the Lord, and he will forgive you."

The apothecary, Benjamin Price tells us, "The air in the town is bad. We must burn fires in all the streets, and wash the walls of the houses with lime water to purify everywhere. Those who have the plague must drink plenty of herb water."

The strange old woman who has come to look after those who are ill, says, "The devil has entered the bodies of the sick. They must place a live toad on the boils."

Some people think she is a witch. Others say she has been sent by God.

The animal-catcher, William Williams says that the
plague is spread by dogs, cats and pigs. His job
is to catch any stray animal and lock them up in
the pound.

Now, no-one knows what to do. The streets are silent because we are afraid to leave the house. The gates of the town are locked, and nobody comes to the market any more. The country people leave food at the gate, and quickly run away.

At first, those who caught the plague were told to stay indoors. John the blacksmith was called to the Widow Howells' house. He was ordered to chain up her door and board up the windows. I could hear the children inside crying, but there was nothing anyone could do.

Later, Father ordered a pest house to be opened,
where all the sick could be taken to be looked after
by Benjamin Price.

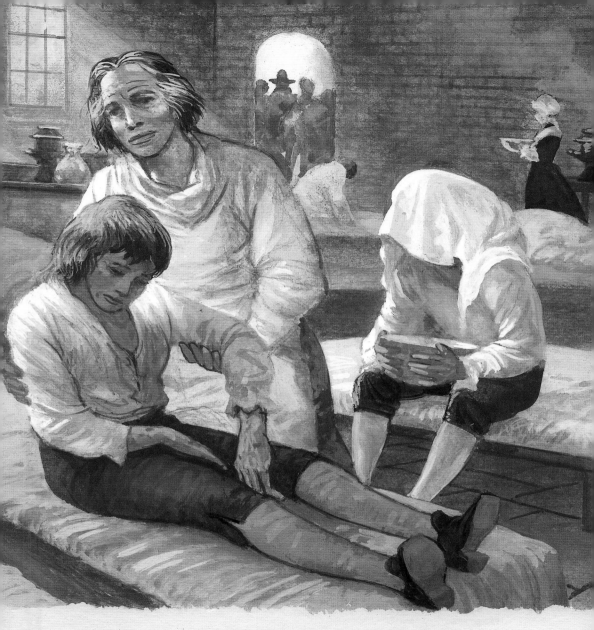

Soon, it became so full that another pest house had to be opened in Cokey Street. There are too many sick people for Benjamin to care for.

At night, I lie in my bed and listen to the rumble of
the cartwheels over the cobbles and the ringing of
the bell. The tar coats are taking the bodies of the
dead to be buried.

All I can smell is the smoke from the fires that burn in the street and the scent of the posy that lies near my bed.

As I sleep, I dream of the time when Father returns from London, and the plague has gone, and I can play once again in the street with my friends.

INDEX